Get Ready!

Learning Simple Sequences

by Lynn Maslen Kertell
pictures by Sue Hendra and John R. Maslen

Scholastic Inc.
New York • Toronto • London • Auckland • Sydney • Mexico City • New Delhi • Hong Kong • Buenos Aires

Tanner was eating his
lunch, but he was ready.

He was ready to play with his
toys! What happened next?

Tanner finished his lunch.
Then he jumped down to play.

Sally was getting ready—ready
to run! What happened next?

Sally put on her shoes. Then
she ran to Tanner's house!

Seth was getting ready — ready to ride. What happened next?

Seth put on his helmet. Then
he scooted to Tanner's house.

Sally and Seth arrived at Tanner's house. What happened next?

They knocked on the door.
"Hi, Sally. Hi, Seth!" shouted Tanner.

The three friends were ready
to play. What happened next?

They did play—
all the way until dinnertime.